Learn Your Times Tables 1

Hilary Koll and Steve Mills

Name

Schofield & Sims

How to use this book

Before you start using this book, write your name in the box on the first page.

You can work through the book in order, learning and practising each times table in turn, or you can choose a specific times table to practise – perhaps one that you have learnt recently or find particularly difficult. The **Contents** page will help you to find the pages you need.

When you have learnt a times table, ask someone to test you. If you know the answers by heart, you can tick the 'I know my ... table' box in the **Summary** section on page 28.

Tips for learning times tables

- Use different voices when reading the times tables facts. You could use the voice of a bird, a worm, a mouse or an elephant. Sometimes shout the facts, sometimes whisper them.

- Clap your hands, tap your head and jump around when you are saying the facts out loud.

- Read the **What to notice** box to find patterns, hints and rhymes that will help you to remember the times tables facts.

- Use the 'look, cover, write, check' method.

- Cut out the flashcards from the centre of this book and practise with them, using the games and activities on page 4.

- Ask someone to test you and test yourself!

You will need:

- a pen or pencil

- scissors

- a stopwatch or clock with a second hand to time yourself.

Contents

Ideas, games and activities

- Cut out the flashcards from the centre of this book and use them in the games and activities below. Keep the cards for each times table in an envelope or folder so that you don't lose them!

- Use the flashcards for one of the times tables. Spread out the cards on a surface, question-side up. Put them in order in a line, starting with ×**0** and going up to ×**10**.

  Say the multiples of that table aloud as you point to each card.

  Then point to any card and give the answer. Turn the card over to check. Repeat until you think you know them all.

- Find the flashcards for one of the times tables. Put them in a pile, question-side up. Answer the questions one at a time. Turn the card over to check. Put the ones you get right into one pile and the ones you get wrong into another.

  Then take each one you got wrong and say the question and answer out loud. Jump up and down as many times as the answer!

- Stick any flashcards you got wrong on to the fridge, bathroom mirror or anywhere you will see it! Have a fact for the day and keep saying it over and over. Ask someone to keep asking you the fact and, when you are sure that you know it, you can put the card away!

- Ask someone else to hold the flashcards in one hand. Ask them to show you a question, holding it up so that they can see the answer on the back. See how quickly you can answer all the questions in a times table. Keep the ones you get wrong and practise them again until you know them.

Get to know the ×2 table

The facts

$0 \times 2 = 0$
$1 \times 2 = 2$
$2 \times 2 = 4$
$3 \times 2 = 6$
$4 \times 2 = 8$
$5 \times 2 = 10$
$6 \times 2 = 12$
$7 \times 2 = 14$
$8 \times 2 = 16$
$9 \times 2 = 18$
$10 \times 2 = 20$

Shout them out!

What to notice

- All the answers in the ×2 table are **even** numbers.

- No answer in the ×2 table will end in **1, 3, 5, 7,** or **9**.

- The unit digits of the answers follow the pattern **0, 2, 4, 6, 8, 0, 2, 4, 6, 8, 0** ...

- The answers are **doubles**.
  For example,
  $4 \times 2 =$ **double** $4 = 4 + 4 = 8$.

- Zero times **any number is** zero.

Getting to know the multiples of 2

The first ten **multiples** of 2 are shown in blue under this line. They are the answers in the ×2 table. Count on in **2s** from zero and say the multiples of 2 aloud.

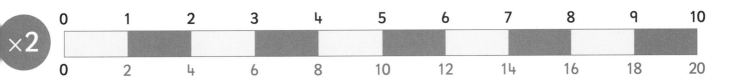

Circle the numbers below that are **multiples** of 2.

13	16	12	7	8	9	18
19	11	5	2	4	14
15	6	17	3	20	10	1

Now say the multiples of **2** in order using a **very squeaky voice**!

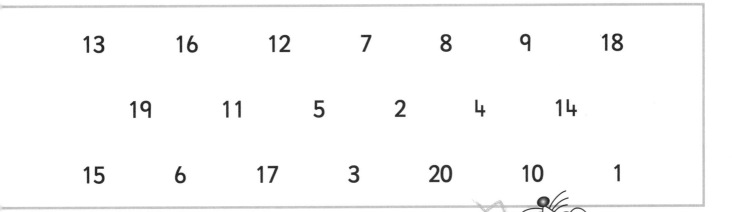

The ×2 table

Look, cover, write, check

Look at the correct answers. Cover them. Write the answers. Now check. Repeat three times.

$0 \times 2 = 0$	$0 \times 2 =$	$0 \times 2 =$	$0 \times 2 =$
$1 \times 2 = 2$	$1 \times 2 =$	$1 \times 2 =$	$1 \times 2 =$
$2 \times 2 = 4$	$2 \times 2 =$	$2 \times 2 =$	$2 \times 2 =$
$3 \times 2 = 6$	$3 \times 2 =$	$3 \times 2 =$	$3 \times 2 =$
$4 \times 2 = 8$	$4 \times 2 =$	$4 \times 2 =$	$4 \times 2 =$
$5 \times 2 = 10$	$5 \times 2 =$	$5 \times 2 =$	$5 \times 2 =$
$6 \times 2 = 12$	$6 \times 2 =$	$6 \times 2 =$	$6 \times 2 =$
$7 \times 2 = 14$	$7 \times 2 =$	$7 \times 2 =$	$7 \times 2 =$
$8 \times 2 = 16$	$8 \times 2 =$	$8 \times 2 =$	$8 \times 2 =$
$9 \times 2 = 18$	$9 \times 2 =$	$9 \times 2 =$	$9 \times 2 =$
$10 \times 2 = 20$	$10 \times 2 =$	$10 \times 2 =$	$10 \times 2 =$

Practise with the flashcards

Cut off the strip of cards for the ×1 and ×2 tables and cut out the cards. Sort them into ×1 and ×2 cards and put them in order.

$$7 \times 1 = 7$$

A number ×1 is **the number itself**.

$$8 \times 2 = 16$$

A number ×2 is **the number doubled**.

Pick any card and say the answer. Turn over the card to check.

Now try these

Write the answers to these questions.

$2 \times 2 =$ _____ $5 \times 1 =$ _____

$6 \times 2 =$ _____ $3 \times 1 =$ _____ $7 \times 2 =$ _____ $9 \times 2 =$ _____

The ×2 table

Hard facts

| 0 × 2 = 0 | Think of this as 'no lots of **2**'.
If you have no lots – you have nothing!
Zero times **anything always equals** zero. |

7 × 2 = 14

Think of **7** as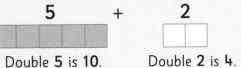

Double 5 is **10**.　　Double 2 is **4**.　　10 + 4 = 14

Double **7** is **14**

8 × 2 = 16

Think of **8** as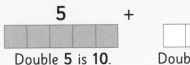

Double 5 is **10**.　　Double 3 is **6**.　　10 + 6 = 16

Double **8** is **16**

9 × 2 = 18

Think of **9** as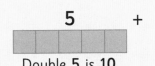

Double 5 is **10**.　　Double 4 is **8**.　　10 + 8 = 18

Double **9** is **18**

Which kite?

Draw lines to join each kite to its owner. See how quickly you can do this.

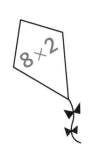
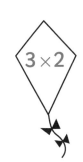

5 × 2 =	7 × 2 =	3 × 2 =	8 × 2 =
3 × 2 =	4 × 2 =	10 × 2 =	1 × 2 =
0 × 2 =	6 × 2 =	7 × 2 =	7 × 2 =
8 × 2 =	9 × 2 =	2 × 2 =	3 × 2 =
7 × 2 =	10 × 2 =	8 × 2 =	6 × 2 =
9 × 2 =	5 × 2 =	4 × 2 =	9 × 2 =
6 × 2 =	3 × 2 =	6 × 2 =	10 × 2 =
4 × 2 =	0 × 2 =	1 × 2 =	0 × 2 =
10 × 2 =	2 × 2 =	9 × 2 =	5 × 2 =
2 × 2 =	1 × 2 =	5 × 2 =	4 × 2 =
1 × 2 =	8 × 2 =	0 × 2 =	2 × 2 =
Time	Time	Time	Time

Here the mix-up man has turned some of the tables.

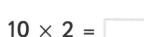

10 × 2 =	2 × 1 =	0 × 2 =	2 × 9 =
2 × 1 =	2 × 2 =	2 × 7 =	2 × 6 =
8 × 2 =	7 × 2 =	2 × 2 =	2 × 4 =
2 × 9 =	2 × 10 =	6 × 2 =	3 × 2 =
2 × 4 =	4 × 2 =	4 × 2 =	2 × 8 =
2 × 2 =	2 × 5 =	2 × 9 =	2 × 2 =
2 × 6 =	9 × 2 =	10 × 2 =	2 × 0 =
7 × 2 =	2 × 0 =	2 × 1 =	10 × 2 =
2 × 5 =	8 × 2 =	3 × 2 =	2 × 1 =
3 × 2 =	2 × 6 =	2 × 5 =	5 × 2 =
2 × 0 =	3 × 2 =	8 × 2 =	2 × 7 =
Time	Time	Time	Time

Get to know the ×10 table

The facts

$0 \times 10 = 0$ ✓
$1 \times 10 = 10$ ✓
$2 \times 10 = 20$ ✓
$3 \times 10 = 30$
$4 \times 10 = 40$
$5 \times 10 = 50$
$6 \times 10 = 60$
$7 \times 10 = 70$
$8 \times 10 = 80$
$9 \times 10 = 90$
$10 \times 10 = 100$

Shout them out!

What to notice

- All the answers in the ×10 table end in 0.

- When we multiply by 10, the digits of a number move across to the left.

H	T	U
		5	×10
	5	0
	1	0	×10
1	0	0

- You already know the ticked facts from the ×0, ×1 and ×2 tables!

Getting to know the multiples of 10

Ten children can sit on a bench.

How many can sit on the benches in these rows?
Count in 10s to find out.

10   20   30   40   40

Now count in 10s as you **clap your hands together!**

The ×10 table

Look, cover, write, check

Look at the correct answers. Cover them. Write the answers. Now check. Repeat three times.

$0 \times 10 = 0$	$0 \times 10 =$	$0 \times 10 =$	$0 \times 10 =$
$1 \times 10 = 10$	$1 \times 10 =$	$1 \times 10 =$	$1 \times 10 =$
$2 \times 10 = 20$	$2 \times 10 =$	$2 \times 10 =$	$2 \times 10 =$
$3 \times 10 = 30$	$3 \times 10 =$	$3 \times 10 =$	$3 \times 10 =$
$4 \times 10 = 40$	$4 \times 10 =$	$4 \times 10 =$	$4 \times 10 =$
$5 \times 10 = 50$	$5 \times 10 =$	$5 \times 10 =$	$5 \times 10 =$
$6 \times 10 = 60$	$6 \times 10 =$	$6 \times 10 =$	$6 \times 10 =$
$7 \times 10 = 70$	$7 \times 10 =$	$7 \times 10 =$	$7 \times 10 =$
$8 \times 10 = 80$	$8 \times 10 =$	$8 \times 10 =$	$8 \times 10 =$
$9 \times 10 = 90$	$9 \times 10 =$	$9 \times 10 =$	$9 \times 10 =$
$10 \times 10 = 100$	$10 \times 10 =$	$10 \times 10 =$	$10 \times 10 =$

Practise with the flashcards

Use the cut-out cards for the ×10 table.

1×10

9×10

4×10

Put the cards in order.

Pick any card and say the answer. Turn over the card to check.

Now try these

Write the answers to these questions.

$3 \times 10 =$ ____ $6 \times 10 =$ ____

$2 \times 10 =$ ____ $8 \times 10 =$ ____ $7 \times 10 =$ ____ $4 \times 10 =$ ____

$0 \times 10 =$ ____ $1 \times 10 =$ ____ $10 \times 10 =$ ____ $5 \times 10 =$ ____

The ×10 table

Hard facts

Watch out for **0 × 10**

| 0 × 10 = 0 | Zero times **any number is** zero. |

The mix-up man

For all multiplication questions, if you swap the numbers around the answer is the same. Look:

$3 × 10 = 30$ $8 × 2 = 16$ $7 × 1 = 7$

$10 × 3 = 30$ $2 × 8 = 16$ $1 × 7 = 7$

Swap the numbers in these questions and write both answers.

$7 × 10 = \boxed{70}$ $6 × 10 = \boxed{}$ $9 × 10 = \boxed{}$

$10 × \boxed{7} = \boxed{70}$ $\boxed{} × \boxed{} = \boxed{}$ $\boxed{} × \boxed{} = \boxed{}$

$4 × 10 = \boxed{}$ $1 × 10 = \boxed{}$ $3 × 10 = \boxed{}$

$\boxed{} × \boxed{} = \boxed{}$ $\boxed{} × \boxed{} = \boxed{}$ $\boxed{} × \boxed{} = \boxed{}$

$2 × 10 = \boxed{}$ $8 × 10 = \boxed{}$ $5 × 10 = \boxed{}$

$\boxed{} × \boxed{} = \boxed{}$ $\boxed{} × \boxed{} = \boxed{}$ $\boxed{} × \boxed{} = \boxed{}$

4 × 10 =	7 × 10 =	3 × 10 =	8 × 10 =
3 × 10 =	2 × 10 =	10 × 10 =	1 × 10 =
0 × 10 =	6 × 10 =	7 × 10 =	7 × 10 =
8 × 10 =	9 × 10 =	2 × 10 =	3 × 10 =
7 × 10 =	10 × 10 =	8 × 10 =	6 × 10 =
9 × 10 =	5 × 10 =	4 × 10 =	9 × 10 =
6 × 10 =	3 × 10 =	6 × 10 =	10 × 10 =
2 × 10 =	0 × 10 =	1 × 10 =	0 × 10 =
10 × 10 =	4 × 10 =	9 × 10 =	5 × 10 =
5 × 10 =	1 × 10 =	5 × 10 =	4 × 10 =
1 × 10 =	8 × 10 =	0 × 10 =	2 × 10 =
Time	Time	Time	Time

Here the mix-up man has turned some of the tables.

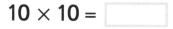

10 × 10 =	10 × 1 =	0 × 10 =	10 × 9 =
10 × 1 =	4 × 10 =	10 × 7 =	10 × 6 =
8 × 10 =	7 × 10 =	10 × 2 =	10 × 4 =
10 × 9 =	10 × 10 =	6 × 10 =	3 × 10 =
10 × 4 =	10 × 2 =	4 × 10 =	10 × 8 =
2 × 10 =	5 × 10 =	10 × 9 =	2 × 10 =
10 × 6 =	9 × 10 =	10 × 10 =	10 × 0 =
7 × 10 =	10 × 0 =	10 × 1 =	10 × 10 =
5 × 10 =	8 × 10 =	3 × 10 =	10 × 1 =
3 × 10 =	10 × 6 =	5 × 10 =	10 × 5 =
10 × 0 =	3 × 10 =	8 × 10 =	10 × 7 =
Time	Time	Time	Time

Get to know the ×5 table

The facts

$$0 \times 5 = 0 \checkmark$$
$$1 \times 5 = 5 \checkmark$$
$$2 \times 5 = 10 \checkmark$$
$$3 \times 5 = 15$$
$$4 \times 5 = 20$$
$$5 \times 5 = 25$$
$$6 \times 5 = 30$$
$$7 \times 5 = 35$$
$$8 \times 5 = 40$$
$$9 \times 5 = 45$$
$$10 \times 5 = 50 \checkmark$$

Shout them out!

What to notice

● All the answers in the ×5 table end in 5 or 0.

● An **even number times 5** will end in a 0.

● An **odd number times 5** will end in a 5.

● Count in 5s and use your fingers to keep track of how many 5s you have counted.

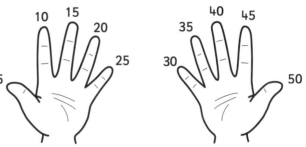

● You already know the ticked facts from the ×0, ×1, ×2 and ×10 tables!

Getting to know the multiples of 5

Write these multiples of 5 in order, starting with **5**.

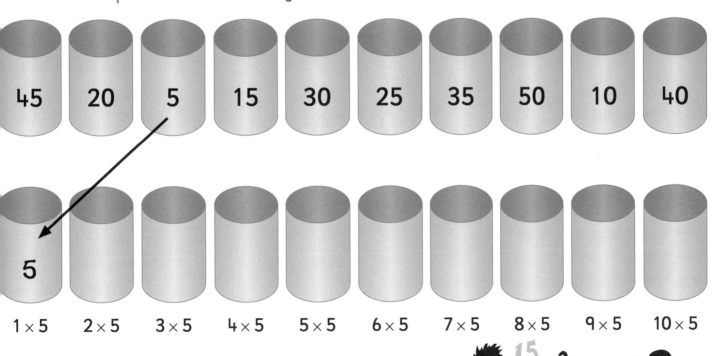

| 45 | 20 | 5 | 15 | 30 | 25 | 35 | 50 | 10 | 40 |

5									
1 × 5	2 × 5	3 × 5	4 × 5	5 × 5	6 × 5	7 × 5	8 × 5	9 × 5	10 × 5

Remember that $0 \times 5 = 0$

Now say the multiples of **5** in order as you **jump up and down**!

The ×5 table

Look, cover, write, check

Look at the correct answers. Cover them. Write the answers. Now check. Repeat three times.

$0 \times 5 = 0$	$0 \times 5 =$	$0 \times 5 =$	$0 \times 5 =$
$1 \times 5 = 5$	$1 \times 5 =$	$1 \times 5 =$	$1 \times 5 =$
$2 \times 5 = 10$	$2 \times 5 =$	$2 \times 5 =$	$2 \times 5 =$
$3 \times 5 = 15$	$3 \times 5 =$	$3 \times 5 =$	$3 \times 5 =$
$4 \times 5 = 20$	$4 \times 5 =$	$4 \times 5 =$	$4 \times 5 =$
$5 \times 5 = 25$	$5 \times 5 =$	$5 \times 5 =$	$5 \times 5 =$
$6 \times 5 = 30$	$6 \times 5 =$	$6 \times 5 =$	$6 \times 5 =$
$7 \times 5 = 35$	$7 \times 5 =$	$7 \times 5 =$	$7 \times 5 =$
$8 \times 5 = 40$	$8 \times 5 =$	$8 \times 5 =$	$8 \times 5 =$
$9 \times 5 = 45$	$9 \times 5 =$	$9 \times 5 =$	$9 \times 5 =$
$10 \times 5 = 50$	$10 \times 5 =$	$10 \times 5 =$	$10 \times 5 =$

Practise with the flashcards

Use the cut-out cards for the ×5 table.

$$8 \times 5$$

$$3 \times 5$$

Put the cards in order.

$$7 \times 5$$

Pick any card and say the answer. Turn over the card to check.

Now try these

Write the answers to these questions.

$10 \times 5 =$ _____ $3 \times 5 =$ _____

$6 \times 5 =$ _____ $2 \times 5 =$ _____ $7 \times 5 =$ _____ $8 \times 5 =$ _____

$0 \times 5 =$ _____ $5 \times 5 =$ _____ $4 \times 5 =$ _____ $9 \times 5 =$ _____

Pull-out answers

Page 5

16	12	8	18
2	4	14	
6	20	10	

Page 6

		$2 \times 2 = 4$	$5 \times 1 = 5$
$\times 2 = 12$	$3 \times 1 = 3$	$7 \times 2 = 14$	$9 \times 2 = 18$

Page 7

$8 \times 2 = 16$	$3 \times 2 = 6$
$7 \times 2 = 14$	$9 \times 2 = 18$
$6 \times 2 = 12$	$4 \times 2 = 8$

Page 8

10	14	6	16
6	8	20	2
0	12	14	14
16	18	4	6
14	20	16	12
18	10	8	18
12	6	12	20
8	0	2	0
20	4	18	10
4	2	10	8
2	16	0	4

20	2	0	18
2	4	14	12
16	14	4	8
18	20	12	6
8	8	8	16
4	10	18	4
12	18	20	0
14	0	2	20
10	16	6	2
6	12	10	10
0	6	16	14

Page 9

40	20	50	60	80

Page 10

		$3 \times 10 = 30$	$6 \times 10 = 60$
$\times 10 = 20$	$8 \times 10 = 80$	$7 \times 10 = 70$	$4 \times 10 = 40$
$\times 10 = 0$	$1 \times 10 = 10$	$10 \times 10 = 100$	$5 \times 10 = 50$

Page 11

$7 \times 10 = 70$	$6 \times 10 = 60$	$9 \times 10 = 90$
$0 \times 7 = 70$	$10 \times 6 = 60$	$10 \times 9 = 90$
$4 \times 10 = 40$	$1 \times 10 = 10$	$3 \times 10 = 30$
$0 \times 4 = 40$	$10 \times 1 = 10$	$10 \times 3 = 30$
$2 \times 10 = 20$	$8 \times 10 = 80$	$5 \times 10 = 50$
$0 \times 2 = 20$	$10 \times 8 = 80$	$10 \times 5 = 50$

Page 12

40	70	30	80
30	20	100	10
0	60	70	70
80	90	20	30
70	100	80	60
90	50	40	90
60	30	60	100
20	0	10	0
100	40	90	50
50	10	50	40
10	80	0	20

100	10	0	90
10	40	70	60

Page 12 continued

80	70	20	40
90	100	60	30
40	20	40	80
20	50	90	20
60	90	100	0
70	0	10	100
50	80	30	10
30	60	50	50
0	30	80	70

Page 13

5	10	15	20	25	30	35	40	45	50

Page 14

		$10 \times 5 = 50$	$3 \times 5 = 15$
$6 \times 5 = 30$	$2 \times 5 = 10$	$7 \times 5 = 35$	$8 \times 5 = 40$
$0 \times 5 = 0$	$5 \times 5 = 25$	$4 \times 5 = 20$	$9 \times 5 = 45$

Page 15

Jack got these wrong:

$7 \times 5 = 35$	$9 \times 5 = 45$
$4 \times 5 = 20$	$0 \times 5 = 0$
$8 \times 5 = 40$	Jack scores 6/11

Page 16

20	35	15	40
15	10	50	5
0	30	35	35
40	45	10	15
35	50	40	30
45	25	20	45
30	15	30	50
10	0	5	0
50	20	45	25
25	5	25	20
5	40	0	10

50	5	0	45
5	20	35	30
40	35	10	20
45	50	30	15
20	10	20	40
10	25	45	10
30	45	50	0
35	0	5	50
25	40	15	5
15	30	25	25
0	15	40	35

Page 18

		$0 \times 3 = 0$	$1 \times 3 = 3$
$7 \times 3 = 21$	$9 \times 3 = 27$	$2 \times 3 = 6$	$8 \times 3 = 24$
$3 \times 3 = 9$	$10 \times 3 = 30$	$4 \times 3 = 12$	$6 \times 3 = 18$

Page 19

$3 \times 3 = $ nine	$7 \times 3 = $ twenty-one
$6 \times 3 = $ eighteen	$9 \times 3 = $ twenty-seven
$8 \times 3 = $ twenty-four	$2 \times 3 = $ six

Page 20

15	21	9	24
12	6	30	3
0	18	21	21
24	27	6	12
21	30	24	18
27	15	12	27

Pull-out answers

Page **20** continued

18	12	18	30
6	0	3	0
30	9	27	15
9	3	15	9
3	24	0	6

30	3	0	27
3	12	21	18
24	21	6	12
27	30	18	9
9	6	9	24
6	15	27	6
18	27	30	0
21	0	3	30
15	24	12	3
12	18	15	15
0	9	24	21

Page 21

32	12	8	
24	16	40	28
36	4	20	

Page 22

	$2 \times 4 = 8$	$5 \times 4 = 20$
$6 \times 4 = 24$	$3 \times 4 = 12$	$7 \times 4 = 28$	$8 \times 4 = 32$
$1 \times 4 = 4$	$10 \times 4 = 40$	$4 \times 4 = 16$	$9 \times 4 = 36$

Page 23

	$4 \times 4 = 16$	$7 \times 4 = 28$
$6 \times 4 = 24$	$3 \times 4 = 12$	$9 \times 4 = 36$	$8 \times 4 = 32$

Page 24

20	28	12	32
12	8	40	4
0	24	28	28
32	36	8	12
28	40	32	24
36	20	16	36
24	12	24	40
8	0	4	0
40	16	36	20
16	4	20	16
4	32	0	8

40	4	0	36
4	16	28	24
32	28	8	16
36	40	24	12
16	8	16	32
8	20	36	8
24	36	40	0
28	0	4	40
20	32	12	4
12	24	20	20
0	12	32	28

Page 25

15	90	12	16
20	9	20	9
24	21	16	70
0	45	8	12
14	10	60	40
5	30	16	12
18	20	27	20
15	0	35	6

Page **25** continued

36	24	90	28
6	30	0	25
27	10	40	6

24	16	0	40
6	9	35	24
45	32	21	18
18	30	0	7
24	15	12	30
25	20	14	12
6	28	100	27
36	8	30	12
8	70	20	4
10	30	0	10
0	40	18	0

Page 26

0	18	14	21
80	18	2	16
9	25	16	9
25	70	15	24
20	30	90	20
28	10	60	30
18	16	18	100
12	8	30	5
0	24	0	8
10	0	5	0
12	2	15	0

30	4	0	45
18	36	100	0
7	9	28	18
10	18	36	70
40	70	12	32
24	15	25	0
45	30	12	3
0	9	24	36
28	45	30	20
18	35	27	16
30	80	8	14

Page 27

25	70	15	24
12	8	30	5
0	18	14	21
80	18	2	16
28	10	60	30
9	25	16	9
18	16	18	100
10	0	5	0
20	30	90	20
12	2	15	0
0	24	0	8

30	4	0	45
7	9	28	18
40	70	12	32
45	30	12	3
24	15	25	0
18	35	27	16
18	36	100	0
28	45	30	20
30	80	8	14
10	18	36	70
0	9	24	36

×4 table	×3 table	×5 table	×10 table	×2 table	×1 table
0 × 4	0 × 3	0 × 5	0 × 10	0 × 2	0 × 1
1 × 4	1 × 3	1 × 5	1 × 10	1 × 2	1 × 1
2 × 4	2 × 3	2 × 5	2 × 10	2 × 2	2 × 1
3 × 4	3 × 3	3 × 5	3 × 10	3 × 2	3 × 1
4 × 4	4 × 3	4 × 5	4 × 10	4 × 2	4 × 1
5 × 4	5 × 3	5 × 5	5 × 10	5 × 2	5 × 1
6 × 4	6 × 3	6 × 5	6 × 10	6 × 2	6 × 1
7 × 4	7 × 3	7 × 5	7 × 10	7 × 2	7 × 1
8 × 4	8 × 3	8 × 5	8 × 10	8 × 2	8 × 1
9 × 4	9 × 3	9 × 5	9 × 10	9 × 2	9 × 1
10 × 4	10 × 3	10 × 5	10 × 10	10 × 2	10 × 1

×1 table	×2 table	×10 table	×5 table	×3 table	×4 table
0	0	0	0	0	0
1	2	10	5	3	4
2	4	20	10	6	8
3	6	30	15	9	12
4	8	40	20	12	16
5	10	50	25	15	20
6	12	60	30	18	24
7	14	70	35	21	28
8	16	80	40	24	32
9	18	90	45	27	36
10	20	100	50	30	40

Schofield & Sims · Learn Your Times Tables 1

The ×5 table

Hard facts

Are you good at halving numbers?
To **multiply by 5** you can multiply by 10 and halve the answer.

$6 \times 5 = 30$	$6 \times 10 = 60$	Half of **60** = 30
$7 \times 5 = 35$	$7 \times 10 = 70$	Half of **70** = 35
$8 \times 5 = 40$	$8 \times 10 = 80$	Half of **80** = 40
$9 \times 5 = 45$	$9 \times 10 = 90$	Half of **90** = 45

Jack's test

Jack has got some of these answers wrong.

Tick which of Jack's answers are correct.

Cross those that are wrong and write the correct answer.

$3 \times 5 = 15$ ✓

$7 \times 5 = 20$ ✗ 35

Name: Jack

$3 \times 5 = 15$	$7 \times 5 = 20$	$9 \times 5 = 50$
$2 \times 5 = 10$	$4 \times 5 = 0$	$10 \times 5 = 50$
$0 \times 5 = 5$	$1 \times 5 = 5$	$6 \times 5 = 30$
$8 \times 5 = 25$	$5 \times 5 = 25$	Score: _____ out of 11

Test yourself: ×5 and 5×

4 × 5 =	7 × 5 =	3 × 5 =	8 × 5 =
3 × 5 =	2 × 5 =	10 × 5 =	1 × 5 =
0 × 5 =	6 × 5 =	7 × 5 =	7 × 5 =
8 × 5 =	9 × 5 =	2 × 5 =	3 × 5 =
7 × 5 =	10 × 5 =	8 × 5 =	6 × 5 =
9 × 5 =	5 × 5 =	4 × 5 =	9 × 5 =
6 × 5 =	3 × 5 =	6 × 5 =	10 × 5 =
2 × 5 =	0 × 5 =	1 × 5 =	0 × 5 =
10 × 5 =	4 × 5 =	9 × 5 =	5 × 5 =
5 × 5 =	1 × 5 =	5 × 5 =	4 × 5 =
1 × 5 =	8 × 5 =	0 × 5 =	2 × 5 =
Time	Time	Time	Time

Here the mix-up man has turned some of the tables.

10 × 5 =	5 × 1 =	0 × 5 =	5 × 9 =
5 × 1 =	4 × 5 =	5 × 7 =	5 × 6 =
8 × 5 =	7 × 5 =	5 × 2 =	5 × 4 =
5 × 9 =	5 × 10 =	6 × 5 =	3 × 5 =
5 × 4 =	2 × 5 =	4 × 5 =	5 × 8 =
2 × 5 =	5 × 5 =	5 × 9 =	2 × 5 =
5 × 6 =	9 × 5 =	10 × 5 =	5 × 0 =
7 × 5 =	5 × 0 =	5 × 1 =	10 × 5 =
5 × 5 =	8 × 5 =	3 × 5 =	5 × 1 =
3 × 5 =	5 × 6 =	5 × 5 =	5 × 5 =
5 × 0 =	3 × 5 =	8 × 5 =	5 × 7 =
Time	Time	Time	Time

Schofield & Sims · Learn Your Times Tables 1

Get to know the ×3 table

The facts

$0 \times 3 = 0$ ✓
$1 \times 3 = 3$ ✓
$2 \times 3 = 6$ ✓
$3 \times 3 = 9$
$4 \times 3 = 12$
$5 \times 3 = 15$ ✓
$6 \times 3 = 18$
$7 \times 3 = 21$
$8 \times 3 = 24$
$9 \times 3 = 27$
$10 \times 3 = 30$ ✓

Shout them out!

What to notice

- To learn the multiples of **3**, count using **'whisper, whisper,** shout!**'** ...
  one, two, three!
  four, five, six!
  seven, eight, nine!
  ten, eleven, twelve! and so on.

- Gradually make your whisper quieter until it can't be heard!

- An **even number times 3** will be even.

- An **odd number times 3** will be odd.

- You already know the ticked facts from your ×0, ×1, ×2, ×5 and ×10 tables.

Getting to know the multiples of 3

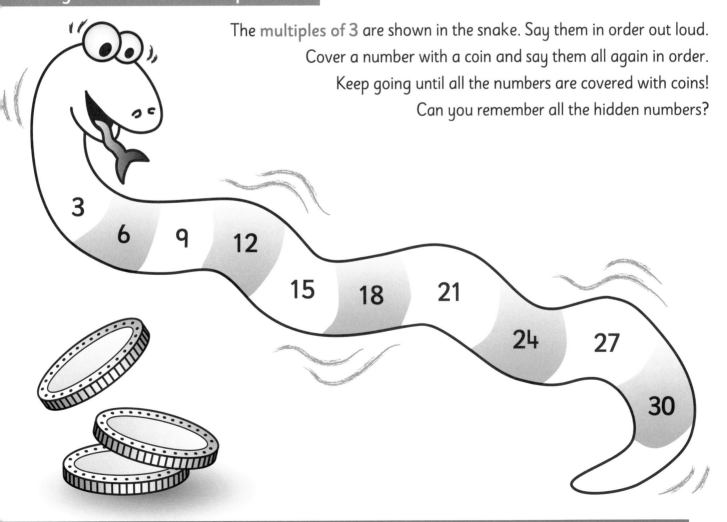

The multiples of 3 are shown in the snake. Say them in order out loud.
Cover a number with a coin and say them all again in order.
Keep going until all the numbers are covered with coins!
Can you remember all the hidden numbers?

3 6 9 12 15 18 21 24 27 30

Look, cover, write, check

Look at the correct answers. Cover them. Write the answers. Now check. Repeat three times.

0 × 3 = 0	0 × 3 =	0 × 3 =	0 × 3 =
1 × 3 = 3	1 × 3 =	1 × 3 =	1 × 3 =
2 × 3 = 6	2 × 3 =	2 × 3 =	2 × 3 =
3 × 3 = 9	3 × 3 =	3 × 3 =	3 × 3 =
4 × 3 = 12	4 × 3 =	4 × 3 =	4 × 3 =
5 × 3 = 15	5 × 3 =	5 × 3 =	5 × 3 =
6 × 3 = 18	6 × 3 =	6 × 3 =	6 × 3 =
7 × 3 = 21	7 × 3 =	7 × 3 =	7 × 3 =
8 × 3 = 24	8 × 3 =	8 × 3 =	8 × 3 =
9 × 3 = 27	9 × 3 =	9 × 3 =	9 × 3 =
10 × 3 = 30	10 × 3 =	10 × 3 =	10 × 3 =

Practise with the flashcards

Use the cut-out cards for the ×3 table.

Put the cards in order.

5 × 3

6 × 3

2 × 3

Pick any card and say the answer. Turn over the card to check.

Now try these

Write the answers to these questions.

0 × 3 = _____   1 × 3 = _____

7 × 3 = _____   9 × 3 = _____   2 × 3 = _____   8 × 3 = _____

3 × 3 = _____   10 × 3 = _____   4 × 3 = _____   6 × 3 = _____

The ×3 table

Hard facts

$$3 \times 3 = 9$$

Remember that **3 × 3** means **3** lots of **3**, which is **9**, not **3 + 3** which is **6**.

$$6 \times 3 = 18$$

6 lots of **3** is double **3** lots of **3**. Double **9** = **18**.

These three facts have answers in the twenties.

$$7 \times 3 = 21$$

Seven times three is twenty-one.

$$8 \times 3 = 24$$

Eight times three is twenty-four.

$$9 \times 3 = 27$$

Nine times three is twenty-seven.

Which question?

Draw lines to show who is answering each question.

3×3

7×3

6×3

9×3

8×3

2×3

Test yourself: ×3 and 3×

5 × 3 =	7 × 3 =	3 × 3 =	8 × 3 =
4 × 3 =	2 × 3 =	10 × 3 =	1 × 3 =
0 × 3 =	6 × 3 =	7 × 3 =	7 × 3 =
8 × 3 =	9 × 3 =	2 × 3 =	4 × 3 =
7 × 3 =	10 × 3 =	8 × 3 =	6 × 3 =
9 × 3 =	5 × 3 =	4 × 3 =	9 × 3 =
6 × 3 =	4 × 3 =	6 × 3 =	10 × 3 =
2 × 3 =	0 × 3 =	1 × 3 =	0 × 3 =
10 × 3 =	3 × 3 =	9 × 3 =	5 × 3 =
3 × 3 =	1 × 3 =	5 × 3 =	3 × 3 =
1 × 3 =	8 × 3 =	0 × 3 =	2 × 3 =
Time	Time	Time	Time

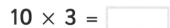

Here the mix-up man has turned some of the tables.

10 × 3 =	3 × 1 =	0 × 3 =	3 × 9 =
3 × 1 =	4 × 3 =	3 × 7 =	3 × 6 =
8 × 3 =	7 × 3 =	3 × 2 =	4 × 3 =
3 × 9 =	3 × 10 =	6 × 3 =	3 × 3 =
3 × 3 =	2 × 3 =	3 × 3 =	3 × 8 =
2 × 3 =	3 × 5 =	3 × 9 =	2 × 3 =
3 × 6 =	9 × 3 =	10 × 3 =	3 × 0 =
7 × 3 =	3 × 0 =	3 × 1 =	10 × 3 =
3 × 5 =	8 × 3 =	3 × 4 =	3 × 1 =
4 × 3 =	3 × 6 =	3 × 5 =	5 × 3 =
3 × 0 =	3 × 3 =	8 × 3 =	3 × 7 =
Time	Time	Time	Time

Get to know the ×4 table

The facts

$$0 \times 4 = 0 \checkmark$$
$$1 \times 4 = 4 \checkmark$$
$$2 \times 4 = 8 \checkmark$$
$$3 \times 4 = 12 \checkmark$$
$$4 \times 4 = 16$$
$$5 \times 4 = 20 \checkmark$$
$$6 \times 4 = 24$$
$$7 \times 4 = 28$$
$$8 \times 4 = 32$$
$$9 \times 4 = 36$$
$$10 \times 4 = 40 \checkmark$$

Shout them out!

What to notice

- All the answers in the ×4 table are **even** numbers.

- No answer in the ×4 table will end in **1, 3, 5, 7,** or **9**.

- The answers are **double** the answers in the ×2 table.

  $$7 \times 2 = 14$$

  $$7 \times 4 = \textbf{double } 14 = 28$$

- You already know the ticked facts from the ×0, ×1, ×2, ×3, ×5 and ×10 tables.

Getting to know the multiples of 4

The first ten **multiples** of 4 are shown in blue under this line. They are the answers in the ×4 table.
Count on in **4**s from zero and say the **multiples** of 4 aloud.

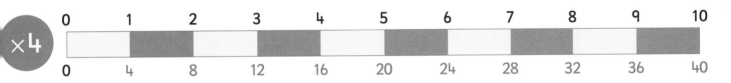

Circle the numbers below that are **multiples** of 4.

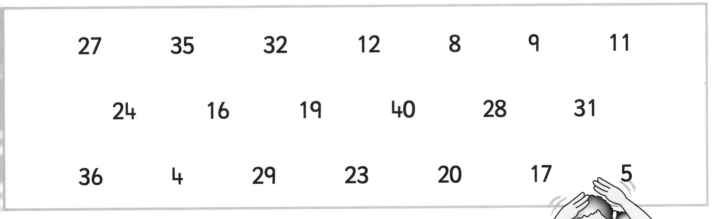

27	35	32	12	8	9	11
24	16	19	40	28	31	
36	4	29	23	20	17	5

Now say the multiples of 4 in order while **patting yourself on your head!**

The ×4 table

Look at the correct answers. Cover them. Write the answers. Now check. Repeat three times.

0 × 4 = 0	0 × 4 =	0 × 4 =	0 × 4 =
1 × 4 = 4	1 × 4 =	1 × 4 =	1 × 4 =
2 × 4 = 8	2 × 4 =	2 × 4 =	2 × 4 =
3 × 4 = 12	3 × 4 =	3 × 4 =	3 × 4 =
4 × 4 = 16	4 × 4 =	4 × 4 =	4 × 4 =
5 × 4 = 20	5 × 4 =	5 × 4 =	5 × 4 =
6 × 4 = 24	6 × 4 =	6 × 4 =	6 × 4 =
7 × 4 = 28	7 × 4 =	7 × 4 =	7 × 4 =
8 × 4 = 32	8 × 4 =	8 × 4 =	8 × 4 =
9 × 4 = 36	9 × 4 =	9 × 4 =	9 × 4 =
10 × 4 = 40	10 × 4 =	10 × 4 =	10 × 4 =

Practise with the flashcards

Use the cut-out cards for the ×4 table.

5 × 4

6 × 4

2 × 4

Put the cards in order.

Pick any card and say the answer. Turn over the card to check.

Now try these

Write the answers to these questions.

2 × 4 = _____   5 × 4 = _____

6 × 4 = _____   3 × 4 = _____   7 × 4 = _____   8 × 4 = _____

1 × 4 = _____   10 × 4 = _____   4 × 4 = _____   9 × 4 = _____

Hard facts

$$3 \times 4 = 12$$

Notice that this fact has digits **1**, **2**, **3** and **4**. Say aloud the rhyme 1, 2, 3, 4 … 12 is the same as 3 times 4.

$$4 \times 4 = 16$$

Think of a square of **4** rows of **4** beans.
Whisper the rhyme 4 times 4 beans are 16.

Use **double**, **double**.

$$6 \times 4 = 24$$

6 doubled is **12**. 12 doubled is 24.

$$7 \times 4 = 28$$

7 doubled is **14**. 14 doubled is 28.

$$8 \times 4 = 32$$

8 doubled is **16**. 16 doubled is 32.

$$9 \times 4 = 36$$

9 doubled is **18**. 18 doubled is 36.

Which dog?

Draw lines to join each dog to its owner. See how quickly you can do this.

Test yourself: ×4 and 4×

5 × 4 =	7 × 4 =	3 × 4 =	8 × 4 =
3 × 4 =	2 × 4 =	10 × 4 =	1 × 4 =
0 × 4 =	6 × 4 =	7 × 4 =	7 × 4 =
8 × 4 =	9 × 4 =	2 × 4 =	3 × 4 =
7 × 4 =	10 × 4 =	8 × 4 =	6 × 4 =
9 × 4 =	5 × 4 =	4 × 4 =	9 × 4 =
6 × 4 =	3 × 4 =	6 × 4 =	10 × 4 =
2 × 4 =	0 × 4 =	1 × 4 =	0 × 4 =
10 × 4 =	4 × 4 =	9 × 4 =	5 × 4 =
4 × 4 =	1 × 4 =	5 × 4 =	4 × 4 =
1 × 4 =	8 × 4 =	0 × 4 =	2 × 4 =
Time	Time	Time	Time

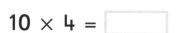

Here the mix-up man has turned some of the tables.

10 × 4 =	4 × 1 =	0 × 4 =	4 × 9 =
4 × 1 =	4 × 4 =	4 × 7 =	4 × 6 =
8 × 4 =	7 × 4 =	4 × 2 =	4 × 4 =
4 × 9 =	4 × 10 =	6 × 4 =	3 × 4 =
4 × 4 =	2 × 4 =	4 × 4 =	4 × 8 =
2 × 4 =	4 × 5 =	4 × 9 =	2 × 4 =
4 × 6 =	9 × 4 =	10 × 4 =	4 × 0 =
7 × 4 =	4 × 0 =	4 × 1 =	10 × 4 =
4 × 5 =	8 × 4 =	3 × 4 =	4 × 1 =
3 × 4 =	4 × 6 =	4 × 5 =	5 × 4 =
4 × 0 =	3 × 4 =	8 × 4 =	4 × 7 =
Time	Time	Time	Time

Test yourself: mixed tests

5 × 3 =	9 × 10 =	3 × 4 =	8 × 2 =
4 × 5 =	3 × 3 =	10 × 2 =	9 × 1 =
5 × 4 =	7 × 3 =	8 × 2 =	7 × 10 =
0 × 10 =	9 × 5 =	2 × 4 =	4 × 3 =
7 × 2 =	10 × 1 =	6 × 10 =	8 × 5 =
5 × 1 =	6 × 5 =	4 × 4 =	6 × 2 =
6 × 3 =	5 × 4 =	9 × 3 =	2 × 10 =
3 × 5 =	2 × 0 =	7 × 5 =	6 × 1 =
9 × 4 =	8 × 3 =	9 × 10 =	7 × 4 =
3 × 2 =	10 × 3 =	8 × 0 =	5 × 5 =
9 × 3 =	5 × 2 =	4 × 10 =	2 × 3 =
Time	Time	Time	Time

3 × 8 =	4 × 4 =	0 × 9 =	5 × 8 =
6 × 1 =	3 × 3 =	5 × 7 =	4 × 6 =
5 × 9 =	4 × 8 =	7 × 3 =	3 × 6 =
2 × 9 =	3 × 10 =	0 × 2 =	7 × 1 =
3 × 8 =	5 × 3 =	4 × 3 =	5 × 6 =
5 × 5 =	4 × 5 =	7 × 2 =	3 × 4 =
3 × 2 =	4 × 7 =	10 × 10 =	3 × 9 =
4 × 9 =	1 × 8 =	3 × 10 =	2 × 6 =
2 × 4 =	7 × 10 =	5 × 4 =	1 × 4 =
5 × 2 =	3 × 10 =	0 × 9 =	1 × 10 =
7 × 0 =	8 × 5 =	6 × 3 =	0 × 0 =
Time	Time	Time	Time

Test yourself: mixed tests

$0 \times 2 =$	$6 \times 3 =$	$7 \times 2 =$	$7 \times 3 =$
$8 \times 10 =$	$9 \times 2 =$	$2 \times 1 =$	$4 \times 4 =$
$9 \times 1 =$	$5 \times 5 =$	$4 \times 4 =$	$9 \times 1 =$
$5 \times 5 =$	$7 \times 10 =$	$3 \times 5 =$	$8 \times 3 =$
$10 \times 2 =$	$3 \times 10 =$	$9 \times 10 =$	$5 \times 4 =$
$7 \times 4 =$	$10 \times 1 =$	$6 \times 10 =$	$6 \times 5 =$
$6 \times 3 =$	$4 \times 4 =$	$6 \times 3 =$	$10 \times 10 =$
$4 \times 3 =$	$2 \times 4 =$	$10 \times 3 =$	$1 \times 5 =$
$1 \times 0 =$	$8 \times 3 =$	$0 \times 1 =$	$2 \times 4 =$
$2 \times 5 =$	$0 \times 0 =$	$1 \times 5 =$	$0 \times 2 =$
$3 \times 4 =$	$1 \times 2 =$	$5 \times 3 =$	$3 \times 0 =$
Time	Time	Time	Time

$10 \times 3 =$	$4 \times 1 =$	$0 \times 2 =$	$5 \times 9 =$
$3 \times 6 =$	$9 \times 4 =$	$10 \times 10 =$	$3 \times 0 =$
$7 \times 1 =$	$3 \times 3 =$	$4 \times 7 =$	$3 \times 6 =$
$2 \times 5 =$	$3 \times 6 =$	$4 \times 9 =$	$7 \times 10 =$
$8 \times 5 =$	$7 \times 10 =$	$3 \times 4 =$	$4 \times 8 =$
$3 \times 8 =$	$5 \times 3 =$	$5 \times 5 =$	$0 \times 8 =$
$5 \times 9 =$	$3 \times 10 =$	$6 \times 2 =$	$3 \times 1 =$
$10 \times 0 =$	$1 \times 9 =$	$8 \times 3 =$	$4 \times 9 =$
$7 \times 4 =$	$5 \times 9 =$	$3 \times 10 =$	$4 \times 5 =$
$2 \times 9 =$	$7 \times 5 =$	$3 \times 9 =$	$4 \times 4 =$
$6 \times 5 =$	$8 \times 10 =$	$2 \times 4 =$	$2 \times 7 =$
Time	Time	Time	Time

5 × 5 =	7 × 10 =	3 × 5 =	8 × 3 =
4 × 3 =	2 × 4 =	10 × 3 =	1 × 5 =
0 × 2 =	6 × 3 =	7 × 2 =	7 × 3 =
8 × 10 =	9 × 2 =	2 × 1 =	4 × 4 =
7 × 4 =	10 × 1 =	6 × 10 =	6 × 5 =
9 × 1 =	5 × 5 =	4 × 4 =	9 × 1 =
6 × 3 =	4 × 4 =	6 × 3 =	10 × 10 =
2 × 5 =	0 × 0 =	1 × 5 =	0 × 2 =
10 × 2 =	3 × 10 =	9 × 10 =	5 × 4 =
3 × 4 =	1 × 2 =	5 × 3 =	3 × 0 =
1 × 0 =	8 × 3 =	0 × 1 =	2 × 4 =
Time	Time	Time	Time

10 × 3 =	4 × 1 =	0 × 2 =	5 × 9 =
7 × 1 =	3 × 3 =	4 × 7 =	3 × 6 =
8 × 5 =	7 × 10 =	3 × 4 =	4 × 8 =
5 × 9 =	3 × 10 =	6 × 2 =	3 × 1 =
3 × 8 =	5 × 3 =	5 × 5 =	0 × 8 =
2 × 9 =	7 × 5 =	3 × 9 =	4 × 4 =
3 × 6 =	9 × 4 =	10 × 10 =	3 × 0 =
7 × 4 =	5 × 9 =	3 × 10 =	4 × 5 =
6 × 5 =	8 × 10 =	2 × 4 =	2 × 7 =
2 × 5 =	3 × 6 =	4 × 9 =	7 × 10 =
10 × 0 =	1 × 9 =	8 × 3 =	4 × 9 =
Time	Time	Time	Time

Summary

×0 table

0 × 0 = 0
1 × 0 = 0
2 × 0 = 0
3 × 0 = 0
4 × 0 = 0
5 × 0 = 0
6 × 0 = 0
7 × 0 = 0
8 × 0 = 0
9 × 0 = 0
10 × 0 = 0

×1 table

0 × 1 = 0
1 × 1 = 1
2 × 1 = 2
3 × 1 = 3
4 × 1 = 4
5 × 1 = 5
6 × 1 = 6
7 × 1 = 7
8 × 1 = 8
9 × 1 = 9
10 × 1 = 10

×2 table

0 × 2 = 0
1 × 2 = 2
2 × 2 = 4
3 × 2 = 6
4 × 2 = 8
5 × 2 = 10
6 × 2 = 12
7 × 2 = 14
8 × 2 = 16
9 × 2 = 18
10 × 2 = 20

×3 table

0 × 3 = 0
1 × 3 = 3
2 × 3 = 6
3 × 3 = 9
4 × 3 = 12
5 × 3 = 15
6 × 3 = 18
7 × 3 = 21
8 × 3 = 24
9 × 3 = 27
10 × 3 = 30

×4 table

0 × 4 = 0
1 × 4 = 4
2 × 4 = 8
3 × 4 = 12
4 × 4 = 16
5 × 4 = 20
6 × 4 = 24
7 × 4 = 28
8 × 4 = 32
9 × 4 = 36
10 × 4 = 40

×5 table

0 × 5 = 0
1 × 5 = 5
2 × 5 = 10
3 × 5 = 15
4 × 5 = 20
5 × 5 = 25
6 × 5 = 30
7 × 5 = 35
8 × 5 = 40
9 × 5 = 45
10 × 5 = 50

×10 table

0 × 10 = 0
1 × 10 = 10
2 × 10 = 20
3 × 10 = 30
4 × 10 = 40
5 × 10 = 50
6 × 10 = 60
7 × 10 = 70
8 × 10 = 80
9 × 10 = 90
10 × 10 = 100

	✓		✓
I know my ×0 and ×1 tables.		I know my ×4 table.	
I know my ×2 table.		I know my ×5 table.	
I know my ×3 table.		I know my ×10 table.	

Schofield & Sims · Learn Your Times Tables 1